1 4.50

Above: Branwen, played by Jo Billenness.
Opposite: Company dances at Neath Abbey as Branwen and Matholwch arrive in Ireland.

On the Tongue of a Bird

The Story of Branwen

Written and devised by the
West Glamorgan Youth Theatre and Dance Company

First Impression 1998

ISBN 185902 527 7

This book is published with the support of the Arts Council of Wales.

Printed in Wales at
Gomer Press, Llandysul, Ceredigion.

The Company is grateful to the poet Gillian Clarke
and to her publishers, Carcanet Press,
for permission to use the poems
'The Starling' and 'Branwen's Grave'
from her book *The King of Britain's Daughter*
(and now available in her *Collected Poems)*
and for her encouragement and workshop
at the start of the project.

Brân, King of the Island of the Mighty, played by Daniel Jenkins.

CONTENTS

The crowd gossip as they wait for Branwen's arrival in Ireland.

DIRECTOR'S INTRODUCTION

The story of Branwen is hundreds, if not thousands, of years older than the written version we have received from the eleventh or twelfth century. Told and retold round the fires in the feast halls, this story, like all those threads which make up the tales of the Mabinogion, was continually reworked and adapted by the professional storytellers and bards.

The story is known to be part of a lost *triad* about the three chief Ancestresses of the Island of Britain and within the almost Arthurian trappings are echoes of a far more primitive tribal society, with their totemic beasts. Brân translates as 'raven', while Branwen is the 'white raven'. There are links to other stories from other cultures, too; Branwen's father, Llŷr, is indeed the King Lear of Shakespeare's play. Actual historical events also feature; Irish communities invaded Wales in the tenth century and settled along the Pembrokeshire coast. In the telling of the story over the centuries, therefore, elements from both contemporary life and the world of legend would have been incorporated at the storyteller's discretion. It was only once it was written down that the story at last became set, and ceased to change in the telling.

On the first day of the residential course when the company met to create this play, the poet Gillian Clarke challenged the Company to rediscover the story for themselves and their audience—to find their own echoes in the fabric of the tale.

In seeking to find the personalities and the motives

that might lie behind the stark words of the written version, the Company has created its own view of the ancient myth, coloured not only by the concerns of the young people themselves about prejudice and racial hatred but also inspired by the historical settings in which the work was to be first performed—the site of two ancient castles and an abbey.

'Her memory erased
from the stones
by the wind and the rain,
her name
on the tongue of a bird.'

The weathered stones of Gillian Clarke's poem became real stones on which actors danced and played their parts.

The Company's desire to be true to the original myth but also produce a compelling piece of theatre was vindicated by the audiences' response to the performances at the three historical sites. The text must now stand by itself, but the following account of the development of the work may inform any plans for future performances, in or out of doors.

Who? When? Where? Why? How?

It was these questions, together with the overriding question for any director, *'Does it work?'* (otherwise phrased as *'Is the audience going to stay awake?'*) that preoccupied the Company during the two-week devising period for the original production.

It was in our first discussions about the myth with Gillian Clarke that the decision was taken to make Brân a young hero rather than a giant. We could have gone for a sixteen-foot puppet, but wished instead to explore the motivations and dilemmas of men and women in a real setting, not in some fantasy world. He was 'a giant among men'. The contrast between the hyperbole of the praise-singing poets and the young boy coping with the realisation that kingship and politics are not as easy as being the hero in the midst of battle, was one we thought we could exploit dramatically. Brân, despite his greatness, is a shadowy figure in the myth, and so we had a session called 'the building of the giant' that gave him the authority and grandeur without needing the height. One of the tasks was then to add more flesh to Brân's character. But as someone said, perhaps these hero figures need to stay in the shadows or we see that they have feet of clay—and where would our giants be then? The missed opportunities for peace, the way Brân cannot avoid the final dreadful carnage, is one of the tragedies of this version of the myth.

The original myth is curiously motiveless. We are never told why things happen. Yet this is the life-blood of drama. The actors must ask themselves, 'Why am I saying these words, behaving like this?' We could not avoid that need to find our own motives for the characters. Branwen's abhorrence of an arranged marriage to an older man is probably anachronistic, but the young people of the Company put their own feelings about such marriages onto the myth. The lack of love, an older man marrying a young girl, and Branwen's

11

stubborn resistance became central to our retelling. If only, in those first nights Branwen and Matholwch were together, love had grown, perhaps the ending would have been different.

Matholwch in this play is therefore considerably older than Branwen and Brân, but we also found him a weak king—not a leader but a follower of his people. His need for peace was seen as a desperate attempt to shore up his power against the numerous petty chieftains of his realm.

Perhaps the greatest challenge for the company was to decide on the reasons for Efnisien's actions. The reason given in the story, that he wasn't consulted, gave us a clue of his jealousy towards his half brother's kingship but we needed something else to account for the enormity of the crime. The neo-fascist dream of the purity of the race and the old hatred of those across the sea who are different, were only too easy to see as being possible motives. In performance, apart from the different accents, we made no difference between Wales and Ireland, thus pointing up the fact that both Efnisien's and the Lady Niámh's hatred is born of their prejudice rather than anything tangible.

It is common in rehearsals to talk about the 'journey' a character makes during the course of the play, to ask, how is each one changed by events? Most of the central characters in this play are changed by events. Branwen realises that personal revenge is not worth the bloodshed. In contrast, Nisien, by the end of the play is more of the fanatic than his brother. His bloodlust and desire for revenge actually took the company by surprise.

One of the casualties of the short devising period was that we would have wished for longer to research thoroughly the background to Celtic tribal life. Another company might make this their starting point. Two areas, however, seemed central to us. First, the fact that women in that society fought in battles and could hold equal place to men in the governance of the tribe. Boudicca was not the only warrior queen. This allowed the women in the company to take much more active roles in the story. Second was the central importance of the host's duty to a guest in Celtic law. To insult a guest, as do both Efnisien, in maiming the horses, and Matholwch, by plotting to kill Brân at the feast, was the ultimate crime, worse than murder in the eyes of all. This is a pivotal motivation within the story. It was only when the company came to imagine the horror of the crime as felt by the Celts that we could understand why the events happened and how much Brân and Matholwch, by ignoring the insults, had fought against the standards of their time in the hope of peace. They did not succeed, but three times they overrode the convention that said a slight to a guest must be avenged.

Two new characters appear in this version of the myth. In the early rehearsals we found that Branwen's part was becoming a series of monologues. We developed the character of the maid in order to allow Branwen to talk to someone, so that subsequently the horror of what was happening to her might be expressed by another person close to her. For Branwen certainly would not have allowed most people to see her pain. The addition of the maid character does mean that Branwen is not totally alone in a foreign land, the loneliness and 'hiraeth' which that position creates in the legend thus being somewhat weakened, but dramatically the middle section of the play seemed to work better for our 'change' to the story.

The Lady Niámh's appearance surprised us all. Her fanatical patriotism matched Efnisien's. In performance, just her presence, never taking her eyes off Matholwch, was motivation enough for many of the events. Her goading presence served to push the weak Matholwch further than he would have gone on his own, allowing no retreat—despite his lust for Branwen. Niámh became the reason for the ill treatment of the young queen. Her whispers of hatred, her thirst for the glory of battle and her hatred of the young Welsh bride who for political reasons had taken her rightful place as Queen of all Ireland, provided an invaluable dramatic tension to the negotiations and the Irish scenes. Branwen grows during the course of her ordeals from a young romantic girl into a tragic character, whereas the Lady Niámh is powerful from the beginning. In the text this strength may not be apparent, as in many scenes a wordless look between her and Matholwch was enough. She appeared late in the devising process but was one of the most powerful characters in the performance.

In any production of this play, a decision will need to be made as to when exactly these kings lived. We came to imagine a Celtic tribal society at some time after the Romans had left Britain: what is known as the Age of Arthur. Brân and the other lord's costumes had elements of a Roman emperor's or general's uniforms in them.

However, because the performances were taking place in medieval castles, in many people's minds the period shifted from Celtic long-hall to castle keep of the very early middle ages. After all, a peasant's dress did not change much over the centuries.

The central aim was to say, 'Here we are and we are telling you a story.' Actors moved instantly from storyteller to lord to peasant. As with all storytellers, their aim was to make the audience work by asking them to imagine, to make the leap from one place to another, or believe that this actor that a moment ago was Welsh was now an Irish peasant. We tried to be honest with our audience and in the end this proved to be the strength of the production. For us, it was useful to keep Brecht's observation in mind, that, 'There are many ways of telling a story, some old, some new, some still waiting to be discovered.' Each company must find its own way of telling the story.

A large proportion of the rehearsal time was devoted to the process of creating real characters among the Welsh and Irish 'people', using clues found in their lines throughout the play. Every actor had both a Welsh and an Irish character with a history, relationship to other servants, attitude to the high ones who controlled their lives and a motivation for saying each of their lines. Thus one girl who at one point is excited by the coming to Ireland of the new queen but wishes for a lover of her own, is one of the most spiteful to Branwen in the rumours sequence when she still has no lover, but by the end is aghast at the loss of all she loves in the final battle.

The outdoor settings with grass underfoot, daylight and sunset to contend with, and no wings or a fly tower dictated the solutions to many of the problems set by the story. In the past, by making use of theatrical darkness, smoke and lighting the company has staged fearsome battles and supernatural effects, but we decided that throughout this production we would not rely on theatrical effects. Save for taking the opportunity to use real flaming torches, this did not seem the time to emulate Spielberg. Another company is welcome to try to add the return of the warriors from the cauldron or the crushing of the hanging sacks or even the maiming of the horses. Indeed, in the devising process we found visual means to depict all these, with the company becoming crushed warriors or the swinging sacks. Several hours in the devising week were spent with the girls 'becoming the horses' but when they were wearing medieval dresses the fine detail of leg or tail twitch was lost and so along with other favourite songs or words it was cut. In the end the style of the show took us to the Greek solution of reportage of the events either by the protagonist or a servant. The actors' belief in what they were telling was so much more powerful in the audience's mind than an obviously fake effect. Often an audience can get out of considering the horror of the act by thinking, 'There's not really a person in that sack' or 'How did they do that?' In performance the words and images were enough.

Throughout, the overriding aim was to ensure that an audience sitting on the grass with their picnics would be clear about the storyline and never need to say, 'Who is that?' 'What is going on now?' Another production is welcome to find their own solutions, whether it be through dance, mime, sound or effect.

Being played out of doors, there were no conventional exits or entrances. Apart from Branwen and her maid needing a costume change into rags, no one left the playing space during the performance. Throughout, all members of the Company were 'parked' on either side of the central space. From there they watched the action, helping the audience concentrate by their own watchful reactions to the action. Their positions and groupings changed as the mood changed, from excitement to suspicion, from defiance to sorrow, according to the story's needs. This also helped keep up the pace of the piece. A storyteller did not need to come *on* for one line, merely take a step forward. When the principal characters such as Efnisien left the action they stood, sometimes watching, sometimes with their back turned to the scenes, from a convenient ruined vantage point, still in view of the audience, still reminding the audience of their presence in the story. Throughout the Irish scenes and the abuse of Branwen, Brân was visible from a high vantage point. From there it was as if he were looking towards Ireland from a high Welsh cliff top, grieving for his lost sister and the lack of news of her.

The play was created by a bilingual company. Throughout the text the reader will find lines in Welsh. A company that does not have access to a Welsh speaker to help with the pronunciation may remove most of these lines, losing a thread of the texture but not the plot,

17

except in scene 15 when it is vital that the young prince does not understand the Welsh his uncle speaks to him.

In performance the piece played for approximately one hour, forty minutes and was played without an interval. If an interval is needed then the duet between Niámh and Branwen's companion, Gwenllian, would make a strong opening to the second half.

A tape of the show and a video is available for any company considering performing the piece. A full music score is also available for hire.

Derek Cobley.

A note on the pronunciation of the names.

Brân has a long '*a*' as in farm.

Branwen has a short '*a*' as in as in 'brand'.

Efnisien the '*f*' is sounded as a '*v*' and the '*si*' as a '*sh*' giving Ev-<u>neesh</u>-i-en.

Nisien the '*si*' is a '*sh*' giving <u>neesh-i-</u>en.

Matholwch the '*w*' is an '*oo*' sound with the '*ch*' softened as in a Scottish '*loch*' giving Math-o-looch.

Lady Niámh is pronounced '*Neave*'.

Gwenllian the '*ll*' is produced by placing the tongue to pronounce '*l*' then emiting breath without voice. (Unless it is spoken by the Irish, who mispronounce it as the '*ll*' in 'all'.)

ON THE TONGUE OF A BIRD

ON THE TONGUE OF A BIRD was first performed by the West Glamorgan County Youth Theatre and Dance Company on the 18th, 19th and 20th July, 1996 at Neath Abbey, Oxwich Castle and Carreg Cennen Castle in association with CADW and the custodians, with the following cast.

The Family of Llŷr

Branwen	Jo Billenness
Brân	Daniel Jenkins
Efnisien	Matthew Thomas
Nisien	Marcus McLean
Gwenllian	Jennifer Walker

The Irish

Lady Niámh	Joanna Williams
Matholwch	Leo Stableford

Storytellers, the people of the Island of the Mighty and Ireland

Leila Adams	Carey Hill
Christian Bradshaw	Luke Hallifax
Ben Daniels	Alison John
Laura Davies	Sophie Lewis
Chloë Dawes	Jordan Lownds
Louise Fermandell	Kirsten McTernan
Mandy Gay	Cathy Miller
Eira Gibson	Jo Needs
Katie Gilbert	Anne-Marie Richards
Beth Glazzard	Karen Skilling
Jo-Ann Gunner	Louise Walker

ON THE TONGUE OF A BIRD

Scene 1—The Irish Ships Arrive.

MUSIC: a solo instrument taken up by others and an informal dance starts bringing in the rest of the company. This merges into company song

Thirteen ships come sailing,
Silken ensigns flying,
Sailing swiftly, sleek and slim,
Fleet through time and tide.

Thirteen ships come sailing,
Proudly 'cross the water,
Sailing on the western wind,
Noble on the waves.

A shield is borne before them,
Uplifted to the sun,
They come in peace these vessels,
Fine ships every one.

Thirteen ships come sailing,
Gleaming in the sunlight,
Sailing with all Ireland's hopes,
'Cross the sea to Wales.

Thirteen ships come sailing,
Silken ensigns flying,
Sailing swiftly, sleek and slim,
Fleet through time and tide.

A shield is borne before them,
Uplifted to the sun,
They come in peace these vessels,
Fine ships every one.

Storyteller 1   The castle of the crowned king, Brân, high on the cliffs above the sea.

Storyteller 2   All those who were powerful in the Island of the Mighty were gathered at his court.

Storyteller 3   There, with his sister Branwen, and his half brothers,

Storyteller 4   The King kept counsel with his Lords, and in the Island of the Mighty there was peace.

(Shouts overlapping from a tower or other high place.)

Lookout 1   Ships !

Lookout 2   Llongau, thirteen ships !

Woman 1   *(from the main acting space)* Sound the alarm.

Lookout 1   No . . .

Lookout 2   A fine fleet . . .

Lookout 1   Thirteen ships!

Lookout 2   There's a shield turned upside down . . .

Woman 2   *(from floor)* A sign of peace . . .

Lookout 1   They come in peace . . . Maen nhw'n dod mewn heddwch . . .

Lookouts   Tell the High King . . . Tell Brân . . .

Lookout 1   Tell Brân .

Branwen   Brân.

> *MUSIC under (Brân appears as 'the hero' above. The rest is spoken proudly, adoringly, exultantly, as a 'praise singer'.)*

Note: the numbers or letters denoting different company members below do not correspond to the lines numbered in any other scene. Each section is renumbered starting from one each time. If fewer actors are available lines can be doubled up. Similarly A-R can be shared between fewer players, depending on the quality of the voice or the needs of the production.

1   Brân, High King of the Island of the Mighty . . .

Branwen   Brân, fy mrawd, King of all the Lands of Britain. My brother.

2   Brân, Bendigeidfran, Brenin arnom ni i gyd . . .

3	Brân, Bendigeidfran . . . the protector of his people . . .
4	The earth raven . . .
5	Brenin Ynys y Cedyrn . . .
6	The blessed peace-bringer . . .
7	Brân the warrior . . .
8	His great sword protects us all.
9	Brân, first in battle . . .
10	Last to leave the feast . . .
11	The bearer of truth . . .
12	The most generous of hosts . . .
13	Brân, the mighty champion . . .
14	Brân, the king-slayer . . .
15	Brân, Bendigeidfran, the breath of his people . . .
16	Leader of a hundred princes . . .
17	A giant among his army . . .
18	The terror of our enemies . . .
19	Fear-slayer . . .

20	Foe-slayer . . .
21	Brân, son of Llŷr . . .
22	Brân, fab Llŷr . . .
23	Brân, Bendigeidfran, of this Island of the Mighty . . .
All	*(Kneeling, as a climax to the praise)* Brân, High King of all the Lands of Britain.
	(Brân and Branwen leave. The rest tell, excitedly, snippets of Brân's life-story.)
A	Brân was clever—Brân was strong . . .
B	Brân when only ten years old dived into the treacherous waters . . .
C	The lady was a long way from the bank . . .
D	He struggled to escape the tangled tresses of the river's pale green weeds . . .
E	Her strength was failing fast . . .
F	Alone he carried her back to the hall, even though it was a mile or more. No one could believe how quickly he reached the great gateway . . .

G   But when Brân turned round, all he could see was a single white bird flying across the sky.

H   When Brân had become a man he was surprised by seven savages from the tribes of the North . . .

I   Brân hit the great stone . . .

J   He fought the twisted evil-eyed dwarf . . .

K   Brân slayed the man . . .

L   He crushed the skull with his bare hands . . .

M   He went down under the twelve men . . .

N   And came up fighting . . .

O   He avoided death once again.

P   Brân climbed the cliff till he could see like a giant in one glance over all his kingdom. As he reached the top he slipped . . .

Q   We thought we were never going to see him again, as he fell through the great hole in the rock . . .

R   But he fought his way back . . .

Ominous MUSIC under following as mood changes back to the real story.

Nisien Brân watched, as the black long-ship, with its carved serpent-headed prow, slid silently up the river.

Storyteller 1 The strangers from Ireland came ashore.

Scene 2—The First Meeting

MUSIC as company disperses and sets up the meeting of the Lords. Four of the Company become Irish and Welsh Lords.

Welsh Lord Welcome to our court. Croeso.

Irish Lord 1 We thank you for that welcome.

Welsh Lord What brings you . . .?

Irish Lord 2 Matholwch the wise, King of all Ireland, seeks an audience with Brân, Bendigeidfran, the mighty King of all the Lands of Britain.

Welsh Lord Your request is accepted.

Irish Lord 2 We thank you.

Welsh Lord What is the business?

Irish Lord 2   We travel with a joyful purpose—the uniting of the Kingdoms of Ireland and Britain, the uniting of the peoples of Matholwch the Wise and Brân the Mighty.

Brân   (*entering*) What is their errand?

Welsh Lord   Matholwch seeks to ally himself with you, my lord.

Brân   Then let him land.

Irish Lord 1   Matholwch has come to ask for Branwen, your sister.

Irish Lord 2   If it seems good to you, he wishes to take the daughter of Llŷr as his bride.

Irish Lord 1   He wishes to unite the Island of the Mighty with Ireland . . . so that they both may become stronger . . .

MUSIC AND SONG cut across. They freeze into a tableau and the rest of company moves onto the stage as they sing. By the end of the song, as the company leaves the stage, Matholwch has joined the group, forming a new tableau. Time has passed by the end of the song and all the negotiations have finished. Niámh is also present, looking on disapprovingly: she hoped the negotiations would fail.

Ships left Ireland's harbours,
Journeyed over waters,
Brân made great a welcoming,
As they reached his shores.

Two Kings met together,
Enemies united,
Calm words passed between the two,
Fortunes sealed by hand.

Now Brân bestows his welcome,
And host is joined to guest,
Two peoples are united,
Blood feuds laid to rest.

Matholwch   So . . . it is agreed?

Brân   It is. I shall meet you again at Aberffraw. There will be great feasting and Branwen shall lie with you. She shall bear a child to unite our two kingdoms.

Storyteller 1   And so it was that Branwen was given to Matholwch.

Storyteller 2   And a time and place were set for him to lie with her.

All leave except for Brân.

Scene 3—Brân and Branwen

Enter Branwen:

Branwen   So I'm to go to Ireland.

Brân   He's a good man.

Branwen   And I'd always dreamt of a young hero . . .

Brân   Better Matholwch than one of those savage chieftains from the North, or a Saxon warlord in the East.

Branwen   But to go across the sea. In the stories our nurse told us, Ireland was always a place of swirling mists and shape-changes.

Brân   If there can be peace between Britain and Ireland then I can relax our guard along all the western shores . . . Our father would have wanted it.

Branwen   I fynd i bendraw'r byd. To go to the edge of the world . . . Does it have to be now? Can't I just be betrothed and then wait a year? It all seems so sudden.

Brân   What good would be served by waiting? His warlords in the hills must be unhappy about the peace now. In a year he might not be able to stand against them.

Branwen	I had thought I might have had a few more years here before . . .
Brân	You're older now than when your mother married.
Branwen	Why has Matholwch never married before?
Brân	Let's be thankful he wants to marry now . . . *(teasing her)* He's heard you're called Branwen the Beautiful.
Branwen	You know I hate that.
Brân	My beautiful sister. Fy chwaer brydferth.
Branwen	Stop it. I wish that the poet who sang those words when I was born had choked on them . . .
Brân	*(changing mood)* You must go. You know I need rest from the raids along the coast. He is rich . . . he has brought a fine string of horses as a dowry gift . . . a stable-full of colts for our Lords. Your child will be High King of Ireland. He has promised to make him his heir.
Branwen	A fi? Beth fydd yn digwydd i minnau? *And me?*
Brân	As his queen you will command his court.

Branwen	I dreamt of a young hero who would pay court to me. We had dreams . . . Has our brother, Efnisien, returned from the north yet?
Brân	*(Shrugs. He knows he should have consulted him.)* It has been decided.
Branwen	When shall I see Matholwch?
Brân	Before the waning of the moon at Aberffraw.

Brân exits on line followed by Branwen.

Scene 4—The News Reaches Efnisien.

Storyteller 1	Nisien, stepbrother of Brân, hurried to tell his own brother, Efnisien, the news of the proposed marriage of their sister.
Nisien	Brother,
Efnisien	Yes?
Nisien	Great news. It reached me this morning—our sister Branwen, betrothed to Matholwch King of Ireland.
Efnisien	What? When did this happen?
Nisien	Angered, brother?

Efnisien	Betrothed? And without so much as a word to ask my consent? My opinion . . .
Nisien	Surely, it is not your place. It is Brân's opinion which is important in these matters.
Efnisien	Brân? You make me laugh! Brân may be King but he is of equal status to us, and it is I, Efnisien, who defends this country's pride.
Nisien	Brân is a born leader, a warrior, a man of honesty and great virtue, a giant amongst men.
Efnisien	But he is . . .
Nisien	You have sworn allegiance.
Efnisien	My loyalties lie in the future of this country. Ireland and Wales united would mean that Irish blood would be in this family forever. Don't you see that? Trust me, Nisien, Ireland must be disgraced for this act.
Nisien	Brother?
Efnisien	He could not have hit upon a greater insult to me. I will repay . . .

Brân	Efnisien! Nisien! We have much to do. Preparations to—
Efnisien	I won't allow it, Brân.
Nisien	Efnisien, now is not the—
Brân	If your brother has something to say, let him say it.
Efnisien	Don't do that! You tell me when to speak, when not to speak. When to think, when to act: you treat me like a child.
Brân	Men of our court, sons of Llŷr, should not behave like this. I'll treat you with dignity when you behave with dignity.
Efnisien	I want to know why I wasn't told. I want to know why you gave away my sister to . . . to them, without my consent.
Nisien	It wasn't like that. You were away.
Brân	If you will only listen. Efnisien, you—
Efnisien	I demand you answer me . . . *(Pause, he has gone too far.)*
Brân	Nisien, take your brother away. Tell him that when he 'asks' what happened, I will tell him. I'll tell him about the need

to act fast, the need to do what I could for the chance of peace in these Islands and for our sister who will now be queen. And when he is sufficiently calm, I suggest you tell him not to demand things of Brân and then, only then, tell him that this outburst is forgotten.

He exits and Nisien, after a rejection by his brother, leaves as well.

Efnisien   Brân could not have hit upon a greater insult than to have given away so excellent a girl as my sister without my consent. An equal insult to the Irish is required to regain my honour, to ensure that she is not exiled to an Irish bog for a futile dream of a united . . . the gift horses! . . . An insult for an insult.

Scene 5—Cutting of the Horses

Stable lad enters with hay bale and sings. The lyrics are based on medieval Welsh lyric poems.

Proud horses, with your tossing manes,
Rest now at peace with plenty,
Wisdom and courage in your hearts,
Strength, that you wield so gently.

Proud horses with your tossing manes,
Memories of ancient stories,
Take the reward so well deserved,
Earned on the fields of glory.

You have faith and trust in your master
Bridled as a friend, not a slave.
Kinship 'twixt the beast and the rider,
You are numbered now 'mongst the brave.

Proud horses with your tossing manes
Eyes are in joy emboldened
Verity shines within your hearts,
Spirits of valour golden.

MUSIC continues, now changed.

Efnisien   They were grinning at me and I wanted to look away but they wouldn't let me . . . all that I could see, their aching grins and their yellow teeth and their dark eyes . . .

(Enter Nisien slowly, unseen by Efnisien.)

I stepped closer . . . slowly towards those eyes . . . It was the future of Britain I held in my hands as I cut deeper . . . dug deeper

Women run on, halt, staring at the blood on their hands and on the horses all round them—horror. (Note: the numbers below do not need to correspond to those in scene 1 or any other scene.)

1	Horses . . .
2	Lips . . .
Both voices	Horses . . .
3	Blood . . .
4	Gwaed . . .
5	Suffer . . .
6	Ears . . .
7	Torri . . .
All 7 voices	Horses . . .
8	Slash . . .
9	Savage . . .

10	Spoil . . .
11	Gouge . . .
All 11 voices	Horses of a Guest . . .
12	Maim . . .
13	Eyelids
14	Revenge . . .
All	Horses . . .
Efnisien	What have I done?
Nisien	Brother, why? Why strike on our guests to ease your jealous mind, your jealous soul? . . . Each innocent creature, peacefully grazing, struck with an evil scream in your heart. Brân is king, therefore it is his decision. It *was* his decision. Why can't you respect that? Everything Brân has done since he has become our King has been for the strength of these islands . . . Your liege, lord, you have sworn him allegiance! Why? . . . to insult our guests . . . a guest should be treasured . . . not this outrage . . . not this Evil . . . Efnisien? *(no answer)* Silence burdens you beneath your bloodied boots.

Efnisien	You expected me to remain quiet, silent, while Brân gives away our sister, the flower of our land? He should have consulted me—it is my right. As his brother—we are both the sons of Llŷr.
Nisien	The sound of screaming still rings in my ears. O, Brân . . .
Efnisien	No one has the right to give away the future of this land. If Branwen had had a child, our country would have been ruled by one who was half-caste . . . The line of kingship would no longer have been pure . . . Mongrel blood, tainted blood in the veins of the descendants of Llŷr. Now that will not happen. For this crime through the ages I will be known as the Insulter of guests, the Cutter of horses, but I am the the Guardian of the Isle, the Saviour of the Land. The insult will drive Matholwch away . . . Blood still on my hands . . . He cannot marry the sister of one who has insulted him so horribly . . . so bloodily . . . his people will not allow it. He must leave without her.
Niámh	(*entering triumphant*) They're preparing the ships to leave. We sail at first light. The Welsh have shown their true colours. We have not gained, no, but at

least we have not lost. *You* have lost your pride and reputation. Matholwch will return to Ireland and seek an Irish bride. *(she smiles)* Those appeasers with their constant talk of peace will be silenced and we can prepare for the time when we can claim Brân's lands.

Efnisien   How can Brân be silent? Not one word of anger . . . not a blow . . . he's treating me like a child.

Nisien   You're his brother, he cannot punish you—banishment and exile will be your future.

Efnisien exits as he sees Brân coming on for the next scene. Nisien joins Brân. Niámh goes to greet Matholwch and watches him like a hawk in the negotiations. Until the cauldron is mentioned it is plain she wishes to leave.

Storyteller 1   But Matholwch did not sail. Instead the two High Kings met in council.

Scene 6—The renegotiation and the giving of the cauldron

MUSIC as groups form up and Kings enter.

This negotiation and the negotiation that follows Efnisien's crushing of the skulls (i.e. scene 15, 'The last chance for peace'), should be staged along similar lines. In both the two kings take the harder path of ignoring advice and trying for a new order of peace. Both times they fail. The two kings are placed on opposite sides of the acting area and move towards each other during the speeches. The one-liners come from Welsh and Irish sides, at random except where specified.

1	The kings still want to talk.
2	After all that's happened.
Niámh	An apology will never be enough. Words can't wipe out the insult.
3	What future can there be?
Brân	Yn enw Ynys y Cedyrn . . .
4	They can't be trusted.
5	Brân knows—his father taught him.

41

6	Trust his judgement.
7	A chance for peace must always be taken . . .
Niámh	Say the cowards and appeasers.
8	A chance of peace rather than the certainty of war.
9	What is there still to talk about?
Storyteller 2	Brân gave to Matholwch,
Storyteller 4	A fine sound horse for every one that had been destroyed,
	Nisien appears with the gifts of plate and staff.
Storyteller 1	A plate of gold as wide as his face,
Storyteller 3	A staff of silver equal to his height and as thick as his finger.
Brân	The insult to you and your people was by one man . . . not me, nor the peoples of these Isles. Will you not accept the gifts as recompense?
Matholwch	The insult cannot be redeemed in gold or silver. For me, perhaps . . . *(He shrugs, Niámh moves towards him)* but for my people . . .

Brân	Efnisien's crime is more terrible for that.
Matholwch	Perhaps Ireland and Britain are destined to forever be rivals for the treasures of the northern seas.
Brân	Such waste. Our peoples should be able to live in peace. I'm . . .
Matholwch	I know your friendship is meant but my people, your brother . . . the scars run deep. We should leave . . . my people have families . . . they are uneasy in a strange land.
Brân	Perhaps I can convince your people . . . *(hesitates)*. We have a relic that once was yours . . .

MUSIC OF THE CAULDRON STARTS

Storyteller 3	Brân possessed a cauldron of great power, into which a dead warrior might be placed and be reborn.
Storyteller 1	In the bubbling waters of the cauldron a man might be reunited with his soul that had fled to the underworld.
Storyteller 4	Once reborn that warrior could never speak, for none could tell of the sights he had seen in the grim regions of the dead.

Storyteller 2 But a king possessing the cauldron would never again lack for troops in battle . . .

CAULDRON SONG and ritual as the cauldron is carried across stage

Bring here your dead,
Fetch the departed,
Feed to the cauldron
And fill it with darkness.

The dead—inside this metal womb,
Departed—silent like a tomb,
The cauldron—filled with stench and rot,
Darkness—stinking, deathly, hot.

Cracks open up,
Pathways to Annwn,
All find their way back,
Through bubbling waters.

Life today—Pair y Dadeni,
Life from the mouth of the cauldron.

Life today—Pair y Dadeni,
Light from the heart made of darkness.

Exit of Company, leaving storytellers and Efnisien alone on stage.

Storyteller 1 Brân gave away the cauldron . . .

Storyteller 4   Confident that the new found peace would make the cauldron worthless.

Storyteller 3   Matholwch knew of the power of this cauldron,

Storyteller 4   Recognised the gift as being a sure sign of Brân's desire for peace . . .

Storyteller 2   And despite the murmuring of his people agreed that the two lands should be linked through marriage.

     Storytellers exit. Niámh enters during the speech that follows.

Efnisien   Now the Island of the Mighty is betrayed . . . to give away the ultimate defence of our realm . . . Now the Irish have the cauldron we can never defeat them. They will have it . . . Matholwch will have Branwen.

Niámh   The Welsh have a certain reputation, ignorant and unwise . . . to give us the cauldron and the sister of their king, served on a rusty platter! In time you will find that we will repay your gifts with warriors from that cauldron.

Efnisien   Brân! Your brain has become infected with this fever for peace! Brân, do you realise what you have done?

Storyteller 3   Banished from the court, Efnisien retreated to the hills

Storyteller 1   And soon there was carousal and celebration in the castles of the Island of the Mighty.

Scene 7- The Wedding

Preparations in various places:

Woman 1   The Irish are coming, we're going to have some fun tonight! *(giggles from girls)*

Woman 2   Girls, girls—a man is all you think of. There'll be no celebration for you if you burn those loaves

Woman 1   Oh, I forgot! *(Sudden panic from the girls as they run off)*

Man 1   An Irish man to take the Lady Branwen. Who'd have thought it?

Man 2   If it stops the raids on our ports, it can't be a bad thing.

Maid   Your cloak, madam.

Branwen   Fetch the glass. I must look my best for
                     this king of Ireland.

Nisien   It's time, sister.

Branwen   Tell them I'm ready.

                     *MUSIC — Cheers—celebratory Wedding
                     dance. Nisien goes to bring in
                     Matholwch and Brân. Branwen is
                     flanked by her husband and Brân and as
                     they are surrounded by the dance, Brân
                     joins Branwen and Matholwch's hands
                     in marriage. At the end of the dance the
                     images of celebration, all around the
                     central figures, freeze as the storyteller
                     speaks:*

Storyteller 4   As the couple looked at each other for
                     the first time they thought:

Branwen   Everyone's happy
                     Kissing my cheek
                     Squeezing my hand

                     Goblets are full
                     Plates are empty
                     Everyone waiting for me

                     To take his hand

Brief burst of jollity then new frozen images of celebration.

Matholwch　　　She stands looking at me.
My fine clothes hang from my
　　　　　　　　　　shoulders
but she sees me, not my jewels,
And she stands looking at me.
The men mutter and fidget for wine,
The new gift-horses whinny and
　　　　　　　　remind us all,
but still she stands looking at me.
(Branwen turns to her brother, pleading)
The Welsh Lords stiffen.
Her brother opens his arms to me,
And she turns and looks at her
　　　　　　　　　　brother,
And what she says to him with her eyes
　　　　　　　　　　I cannot see.

Branwen　　　I see glassy eyes of strangers,
Twisted smiles of friends.
In the food the freshness is lost,
The wine has been replaced by vinegar,
And fear balances on the blade of the
　　　　　　　knife in my pocket.

MUSIC. They move together and are surrounded by the dance which restarts. Branwen and Matholwch are left as the dance takes everyone off. Matholwch embraces Branwen. She passively stands as she speaks:

Branwen I feel vulnerable but he holds me close . . . I breath deeper, inhale, exhale and in the dark we stay silent, apart.

Matholwch *(moving away from her, already rejected)* It is time to board the boats. I have great business to do in Ireland. *(He moves away, as Brân and Nisien enter to say goodbye.)*

Nisien As long as the skies bring rain may you be happy. Cymer ofal.

Brân Ffarwél fy chwaer, a chofia, bydda' i yma er dy fwyn. As long as the waves wash onto our shore, may you be safe.

Branwen As long as the birds can sing, I hope my land remembers. Fydda' i byth yn anghofio.

Matholwch Come, the wind is rising. *(Branwen moves to Matholwch)*

Scene 8—Journey To Ireland.

MUSIC. Some of the company form the ship while others dance the journey that takes Branwen and Matholwch to Ireland in the middle of which is Branwen's song:

Storyteller
Yn syth, o'i phriodas wen,
O'i bro ar unwaith aeth Branwen;
Hwyliodd a'i gŵr, Matholwch,
Ymhell o'r castell mewn cwch.

Branwen *(sings)*
Abrasive winds, tear at my eyes,
Pull at my dress, their grip so tight,
Drag me away, away from home,
But I'm too proud, I'm too proud to cry.

Waves crash against the polished deck,
Sea water scours my face.
The spray on my cheek like salty tears,
But I'm too proud, I'm too proud to cry.

My brother stands upon the shore,
His hidden tears behind his smile,
I look ahead, the future calls,
But I'm too proud, I'm too proud to cry.

There follows a dance that symbolises the arrival in Ireland.

50

Scene 9—The Arrival In Ireland And The Year Of Peace.

There are shouts of 'Ireland!' as the boat arrives. A group of servants crowd at a vantage point to see their new Queen arrive.

Steward (*Despairingly without much hope as he follows them*) Scum, all of you, you should be flogged. Get back, get back to work, there . . .

Irishman 1 (*grabbing a girl for a kiss.*) You're worth four horses to me.

Irish maid1 Four horses, only four horses? How many did Matholwch lose for Branwen?

Irish gossip 1 Perhaps she is as beautiful as they say.

Steward What a way to welcome back your king and his new bride . . .

Young Maid 2 Our king with a beautiful young queen, who'd have thought it?

Woman 1 (*to a musician*) Your purse will be full from now on . . . Matholwch's court will be filled with songs.

51

Irishman 2   No more waiting for those endless debates in Matholwch's council to finish. He'll not want to hang around now he's got a young bride to entertain.

Irish gossip 1   How many Welshmen will she bring with her? We'd better all start to like leeks.

Irish gossip 2 *(singing quietly)* Taffy was a Welshman
                                            Taffy was a thief

Steward   Do you want to go back to the bog you came from?

Woman 2   *(Squeezing in from the back)* We're not too late, are we?

Maid 3   A new queen . . . My grandmother wants me to tell her everything about her.

Woman 2   You'll not be able to tell her anything if we don't hurry. We'll be stuck at the back of the crowd.

Irish gossip 2   Seventeen gnat bites.

Woman 2   Could have been worse.

Irish gossip 2   Next time anyone asks me to come down to the river to see the sunset behind the hills, I'll say no.

Irish gossip 1   He's a good man.

Irish gossip 2 But you should see the places where they bit me.

Irish gossip 1 I don't think I want to.

Woman 2 She's arriving today, no river banks for her.

Irish gossip 2 Branwen the Beautiful on her rich ship.

Irish gossip 1 A beautiful Welsh woman? Hardly seems possible.

Irish gossip 2 I wonder if she gets gnat bites?

Irish gossip 1 I should imagine they're the most beautiful gnat bites you've ever seen.

Irish gossip 2 Maybe that's why he married her, for her gnat bites.

Irish gossip 1 Nah.

Irish gossip 2 But what if she turns out to be 'the downfall of the country'?

Woman 2 We're on our way down anyway.

Irish gossip 2 'Branwen the Beautiful' or not, I wouldn't like to be blamed for the Downfall of Ireland.

Woman 2 Is that what the poets are saying?

Irish gossip 1 It's the food.

Irish gossip 2 /Woman 2 What?

Irish gossip 1 Rots the brain . . . they eat seaweed and snakes.

Woman 2 They're a strange race, so they are.

Irish gossip 2 /Irish gossip 1 True.

Woman 2 I've often wondered what makes people eat strange things.

Irish gossip 1 There was a man down the lane who had a goat who ate everything.

Woman 2 Matholwch must be blind—no, not blind— stupid.

Irish gossip 1 Heresy. It's heresy, it is.

Young maid 2 A new queen . . . Ireland will be reborn.

Woman 3 He's chosen wisely. The poets have been singing her praises since her birth.

Young maid 2 I wish a poet would sing my praises.

Woman 3 You're not one of 'The Three Beautiful Queens Of Wales'.

Irishman 3 Poets only praise those who pay for their supper. You couldn't afford a verse let alone a song.

Young maid 2   I can dream a poet might fall in love with me.

Woman 3   Not now our Irish poets have Branwen to adore.

Woman 4   'Matholwch the Lover.'

Woman 5   No . . . Matholwch the Peacemaker, more like.

Woman 4   That's true, we won't have to watch the Eastern seas for raiders anymore.

Woman 5   Trade should improve now the ships can get through without fear of those Welsh pirates.

Woman 2   There she is . . .

Irish Maid 3   He seems younger . . .

Irish maid 1   A new dawn for all of us.

Matholwch and Branwen and entourage enter. Dance of welcome.

storyteller 2   The young village daughters doting, excited.

storyteller 1   A new face arrives, wide eyes filled with tears.

storyteller 3   The people loved their new queen at first sight. Gifts to her filled the courtyard.

storyteller 2   For the first year the people sang her praises.

storyteller 4   Every great man or woman that visited Branwen would be given a gift—

storyteller 2   of a brooch,

storyteller 3   or a ring,

storyteller 2   or a treasured royal jewel,

storyteller 1   and she spent a year of great fame, living with honour among friends,

storyteller 4   and in the course of that year Branwen gave birth to a child.

                      MUSIC as Matholwch and Branwen and Company leave.

Gwenllian   When I first heard the news I was to go to Ireland I felt scared. What if I don't like it over there? What if they don't like us? What if we don't fit in? But my fears were . . . Well, I needn't have worried at all . . . I was still with my mistress and those who didn't like us must have kept

56

quiet when she or the King were around. Although I could tell Branwen longed to be back home . . . As the baby grew inside her, she blossomed . . . the bond needed between Wales and Ireland . . . one little baby . . . I remember I took some sheets to her room,

(Lullaby version of final song sung by Branwen heard softly under)

I stopped at the door and looked in. She didn't see me. She was sitting at her window looking out at the sea . . . she had one hand resting on her stomach and she was singing a lullaby and smiling . . . It'll give her something to . . . love . . . *(She realises Branwen should already have a husband to love)* to call her own dear. It affected everyone—we were all more cheerful, not grumbling . . . until that was . . . just after the birth of the little prince, the murmuring began. Efnisien's insult was dragged up again.

Servant 1   *(entering)* Welion or whatever your name is? Why can't you Welsh have simple names a person can pronounce? Your mistress wants you. *(Exit both)*

Scene 10—Rumours

Storyteller 3   With the birth of the child, the old insults, never quite forgotten, began to be picked over like an old scab that had never quite healed.

Niámh   *(spreading rumours and agitating among the lower orders)* Matholwch might be able to live with the insult but that child will carry the taint down through the generations.

Servant 2   The 'United Islands' were always a dream dreamt only by Matholwch.

Servant 3   When that child is grown up, you mark my words, he'll be over in Britain, and we'll be forgotten.

Servant 2   We'll be a king-less lump of rock on the edge of nowhere.

Servant 4   Our tithes and taxes will go to pay for their wars.

Niámh   And our men will go too . . .

Servant 2   She's given him a Welsh name.

Servant 4   Gwern. It probably means 'an insult to Ireland'.

Four or five serving women enter—
Giggles and whispering out of which we
hear:

Servant 5   Who told you that?

Servant 6   A certain soldier who stands guard—she
never goes to his bed.

Servant 7   Would you want to go to Matholwch's
bed?

More giggles and then silence as
Branwen and Gwenllian pass by them.

A   The rumours, mutterings and slanders
sing in the silence
after the spitted gossip of the kitchens.

B   They are stirred into the steaming
cooking pots over the fires.

C   They are reflected from faces by the
clattering pots.

D   They leak from the tongue
of the watching women,
staining the pinnies of young girls
in the steamy kitchen.

E   They are beaten into the rushes
and dirt on the floor.

F	Hidden in the storerooms and stables.
Gwenllian	They are passed on in draughty corridors outside a closed door, behind which a young girl silently weeps in an empty room where she is left alone.
Servant 4	*(calling)* Madam! *(Branwen exits)*
Gwenllian	You can read their hatred in their soft deceiving words . . . *Small group forms, one sewing a rich dress.*
Maid 1	Ow!
Maid 3	What's wrong?
Maid 1	Blood on the dress now—pricked my finger!—and it's so heavy.
Maid 2	What I'd give for a dress like that . . . Welsh whore!
Maid 3	She arrives and everything is done for her.
Maid 1	And does she notice? That will do . . . what do I care if she complains that the stitches aren't straight?
Maid 3	She wouldn't dare.
Maid 2	He must be blind.

Maid 3	Well, I'm not one to gossip . . .
G	Each stone of the castle whispers it, every hidden shadow declares it.
H	Rumour is sown with the corn and time spreads it further.

Two servant girls prepare vegetables:

Woman 1	Our Benjamin's they were.
Woman 2	Benjamin's? What, those pigs wandering all through the kitchens? Big, they were, weren't they?
Woman 1	Fat.
Woman 2	Welsh pigs are fat—like their Queen.
Woman 1	She's got an 'admirer' already . . . shows you what she thinks of our king.
Woman 2	Maybe it was one of her troop who let them out . . . the pigs . . . you never know with a Welshman . . . Pass me that, will you? *(points to knife)*
Woman 1	This?
Woman 2	She had the nerve to bring all her own servants. We weren't good enough.
Woman 1	Probably because no one can understand a single word she says.

Woman 2	Like a bunch of leprechauns they are, granting all the men's wishes. All a bunch of whores . . . first minute they got here . . . giving the eye to our men . . .
Woman 1	I soon put an end to Benjamin's little eyeful.
J	A nudge, a wink, a smile,
K	There is twisted enjoyment in the stares.
Woman 3	Branwen the Beautiful!
Woman 4	The colour's going out of her cheeks.
Woman 5	There won't be a second child.
	Matholwch enters, centre.
Niámh	I fill a goblet and hand it to him. Slander swallowed with the red wine, In Matholwch's goblet, In the veins of Matholwch, As the red wine seeps through his blood, Into the poisoned chalice of Matholwch's mind.
Matholwch	The wine tastes of vinegar and there's no freshness in the food any more.
Woman 6	He thought everyone would forget.
Man	Yes.

Woman 6	But you can't change the blood.
Man	You can tell he's not happy.
Woman 6	The insult still grates.
Man	Every time he walks past the stables, he's reminded.
A	It was kept in the locked box behind closed doors at the bottom of his heart.
Gwenllian	The rumours are no secret, for it's told to the sky. It's too loud for it not to be heard.
A	*(to Gwenllian)* It carries on the wind, advances with the tide, wicked words drift across the open sea but the wind blows them back. They will never reach Wales.
	All leave Gwenllian alone as Branwen enters.
Branwen	I look at the image of my own face in the mirror and I ask the question: 'What more can I do?' I rub my finger on the blade of the knife in my pocket. Efnisien, what have you done? . . . I have never been at home here. Even the baying hounds refuse to know their mistress. I walk the cliffs listening to the

bleat of angry sheep, watching the sun rise from the sea, staring East, to Wales across the sea.

Gwenllian   Longing to be . . .

Brân   *(from his high post)* As children we would sing, my gentle sister and I. The corners of the castle would fill with her happy song. Our happy song. Now our home is heavy with a silence. She is gone.

Matholwch   *(entering with Niámh)* I wake in the night—alone in the cold bed, to the sound of thundering hooves. In the puddles made by the feet of the passing army, in the swirling mists, I see the heads of the horses . . . in the pitying faces of the watching women, I am reminded.

Group   The trees whisper it to the waves
    and the waves wake the lightning
    and the lightning strikes the sea
    and the sea erupts in anger
    and the anger crashes over the land.

Niámh   *(sarcastic, talking partly to Matholwch, confident in her power over him, partly as if he were not there.)* Matholwch. Oh, what a great man! So strong and so wise, leading his country into the path of glory! Leading his country to ruin. He's a man with so much power . . . think what he could have done—could still do with it. He sat and listened, passive to the dream that Britain, that Isle of the Mighty and our Green Isle could have become united. He takes his orders from those who should have no business meddling in his affairs, people unable to judge, unfit to govern.

MUSIC of Unease, Threat and Rumour as background to the speech.

Oh, what a great country, a child born, a tainted child, a child conceived to carry the insult. Matholwch lies with the sister of the man who caused the insult. But he's beginning to listen, he's listening to the ones that know . . .

Matholwch   Organise, Matholwch, organise . . . think.

Company slowly gather round Matholwch and speak his thoughts or put pressure on him as councillors and people.

Niámh   You have made a pledge always to listen to your people. A king with ears of stone is soon a tyrant.

Matholwch   Good, good . . .

65

Thought 1	Your people point to the slight against them. Your people say Branwen might be beautiful but—
Matholwch	That's true . . . Branwen is beautiful, she smiles and my soul burns. My head is clouded by a single sense of her . . .
Thought 2	Think . . . be objective, be a wise leader. Country first, self later.
Matholwch	Right!
Niámh	You have been looking, asking and listening. Matholwch the Wise, your people have pointed and you have seen—
Matholwch	Nothing . . .
Niámh	At first. But perhaps that is a testament to her cunning. Blinded by Branwen the Beautiful! But notice then a misplaced laugh, that smile . . . Those close to her are so obedient, have such blind faith . . . Branwen the Cunning! Is it right that she should command so much respect close to and utter hatred from those outside? Outside where sight is not hindered by proximity.
Thought 3	We know the Welsh have a capacity for deceit. Again and again, your mind turns

back . . . The horses . . . those good horses. All those trusting faces. Who knows what Branwen's face conceals?

Matholwch   *(sighs)*

Niámh   You cannot bind with frayed rope. The child is not an heir, he carries a taint . . .

Matholwch   You cannot bind with frayed rope . . . Nice, I shall have that written.

Thought 4   Power rests in confidence. The confidence of ruler and country. When the confidence is gone, the country is lost . . . and so is the king. Your country, your rule . . . we cannot withstand a further dent to our pride.

Thought 5   Brân and Branwen are all a brother and sister should be. They are united, they have a foothold in your country . . . scandal could swallow us whole into Britain.

Niámh   Branwen, rather than joining—

Thought 1   Poses a threat . . .

Niámh   Proves a useful weapon to her brother.

Matholwch   Decisions . . . Decision . . . Call Branwen—*(Everyone leaves the stage* *clear.)* I . . . I . . . would speak with her, *(Branwen enters)* Country first, self later . . . Branwen?

Branwen   As I came in I heard the kitchen maids and—

Matholwch   Branwen.

Branwen   Yes?

Matholwch   Nothing.

Branwen   Did you know there was a storm coming?

Matholwch   *(to himself)* Yes, I've known all along.

Branwen   The horses are going wild. For a moment I thought I was back in Wales. I used to visit the stables every day when I first arrived You know how unsettled horses get in a storm. *(Matholwch strokes her neck, she does not respond.)* Brân used to go walking. I was too young to go but he'd tell me what he'd seen. To me it seemed he controlled the weather. When he got angry my beautiful world was thrown into disorder. The clouds would gather around his head . . . but then I would sing to him or it would rain and

68

the anguish would go away. Why don't you let me sing to you? This storm is different. I was talking to Gwenllian in my chamber and . . .

Matholwch Oh yes, we all know what you talk about in your bedroom.

Branwen What?

Matholwch You know.

Branwen Don't you see what you're doing to me? . . . I'm your Queen, you're my husband.

Matholwch I never realised you thought of me as a husband.

Branwen You are the father of my child.

Matholwch Can I be sure of that? When we were married our hands were joined by gold and our hearts? By duty? . . . Never was a husband more reasonable. I opened my heart to you and hoped to find your love but instead . . .

Branwen That's just an excuse . . . you're using it because you can't bring yourself to . . . Is this what you want? . . . or your people?

Matholwch   You know what I'm accusing you of
. . . There are many reasons why . . . You
have disgraced my land . . . I do not
know what behaviour is thought fit for a
queen in Wales, but an Irish Queen—

Branwen   There was no need for that: my brother
rules a court that is respected throughout
the land.

Matholwch   Not in my land it's not. He cannot even
control his own brother . . . I will not
tolerate rebellion in my country. My
people demand vengeance upon you for
the offences of your brother and you—

Branwen   If you cannot control your own people,
my Lord, then perhaps we are both
unsuited to sit upon a throne.

Matholwch   The king's title is hereditary but the
queen's is not.

Branwen   Are you accusing me? I've been faithful
to you for as long as I have been in
Ireland.

Matholwch   The people are saying that the white
raven is not as pure as I thought it was . . .
I've heard that whatever Branwen the
Beautiful does, she will never—

Branwen   Perhaps the Great High King Of Ireland is not as strong as—

Matholwch   Branwen! I think you had better be quiet!

Branwen   It shall be as my lord orders.

Storyteller 4   Matholwch, unable to face Branwen, arranged it so that he was away on a hunting expedition.

Storyteller 1   Then his steward took Branwen from the royal apartments.

Storyteller 3   It was proclaimed that from that day she was to work and live in the kitchens.

Company form the corridor of watching servants.

Storyteller 2   The people stared as she walked through the passages to the kitchens but Branwen said nothing, uttered no word of complaint.

Branwen   It shall be as my Lord orders.

She exits between the scornful watchers.

Matholwch   When rumours take flight a king must clip their wings.

Scene 11—Exile of the Exile.

Niámh and **Gwenllian** *(sing duet)*

Niámh   Eyes stare through her,
                    Sharpened fingers scratch her face,
                    Hate-filled murmurs,
                    Servants laugh at her disgrace.

Gwenllian   But she's too proud to cry,
                    She's too proud to cry.

Niámh   Eyes stare through her,
                    Bitter words and hearts of stone,
                    Anger mounting,
                    She must always be alone.

Gwenllian   But she's too proud to cry,
                    She's too proud to cry.

Brân   *(from high point)* I stand at the edge of
                    my land, and as I breathe in the evening
                    air I listen to the sound of the sea that
                    arrives from Ireland . . . And my heart is
                    pierced by the sound of laughter. . . . Oh,
                    Branwen . . . I still remember.

Niámh and **Gwenllian** *(sing duet)*

Gwenllian   Eyes stare through her,
                    Stabbing at her fragile heart,
                    Taunting, gloating,
                    Anguish tearing her apart.

Niámh   We'll grind her down, we'll make her cry.

Both alternating	She'll never win, we'll make her cry, She'll never win, we'll make her cry.
Gwenllian	Can't you show her pity? I'd gladly suffer with her, for her, But she's too proud to cry, She's too proud to cry.

They both exit. Servants busy with daily round of tasks enter.

Storyteller 4 Ond rhai hyll fu'n taro hon.
A'i hyrddio hi'n Iwerddon
I hen gell, yn forwyn gaeth,
I aros yn ei hiraeth.

Servant 1 Ugly Welsh mare!

Servant 2 The other day I asked her to pass me a jug and she completely ignored me. Can you believe that?

Servant 4 She burnt the bread again yesterday.

Branwen enters—now in rags, carrying firewood.

Servant 2 Welsh bitch.

Servant 4 You know who this is, don't you, ladies? This is Branwen the Beautiful.

Servant 5 Not so beautiful now.

Servant 6 She's fat and ugly like a crow. *(pushes/trips Branwen, who drops her sticks.)*

Branwen   *(involuntarily)* Help me . . .

Servant 7   A woman of no virtue.

Servant 8   Help you? Help you! I've got enough with my own work to do.

Servant 9   Useless.

Servant 2   You can't do anything right, can you? You stupid —!

Servant 4   Have you cleaned the pots? No, you haven't, because I've just had to check.

Servant 10   Why haven't you washed those dishes? I asked you hours ago.

Servant 3   You haven't brushed the floors.

Servant 5   The bread was flat. Why do we have to have flat bread?

Servant 1   She burnt the bread.

Servant 8   All of it?

Servant 9   All of it.

Servant 7   Burnt bread for supper then.

Servant 4   She's so beautiful that she has to stay locked in here all day 'cause no one wants to look at her.

Servant 10   You've taken Matholwch from us.

Servant 9   Branwen the Beautiful.

Insults build to a torrent including insults from before and new ones, that are silenced by:

Branwen   Merch Llŷr, chwaer Brân—
wnaiff neb gymryd hwn oddi wrtha' i.
Fydda' i byth yn anghofio.

Company leave, some ashamed, some smirking, most unrepentant.

Storyteller 3   Matholwch banned all trade with Wales. No ship, ferryboat or coracle was allowed to travel there lest Brân should hear of Branwen's treatment.

Storyteller 2   If any ship from Wales landed, all aboard were to be imprisoned.

The stage clears, leaving Branwen alone:

Branwen   Then it will always be like this . . . bare, cold stone floors, the smell of damp . . . They look and stare . . . I know that . . . Smoke coils up from the fires and chokes me and my tears. I heave in the heavy air damp from the endless drying washing . . . I can smell the freshly cut hay from the window.

Gwenllian enters, now in rags as well.

Branwen	Well?
Gwenllian	No. They caught me talking to a fisherman. *(In hugging her Branwen realises she has been hurt)*
Branwen	Did they whip you? *(They sit close to each other)*
Gwenllian	No one will help me get a message to Brân.

In taking a hand to comfort her, Gwenllian causes Branwen pain and she winces.

Gwenllian	What's wrong with your hand?
Branwen	It's nothing. The hot water burns the blisters on my fingers. My hands were not hardened like yours when I was a girl. I close my eyes and breathe in the hope that soon my brother will come.

(sings)

The sun is sinking,
Drinking up the sea,
In my mind the sky is empty,
I don't want you,
You don't need me.

My eyes are burning,
Yearning for my home,
In my mind my brothers hold me,
No one told me,
No one warned me.

The servants staring,
daring me to cry,
In my mind I cannot see them.
There is no love,
no peace, no hope.

Watching the bleak horizon,
Waiting, hoping . . .

Enter servants.

Gwenllian Leave her alone.

Servant 1 Who are you to tell us what we should do?

Servant 2 What did you do in Wales, young lady?

Gwenllian I . . . I . . .

Servant 1 Lady-in-waiting . . . Nah, a common servant like the rest of us.

Servant 3 Where's your queen now?

Servant 4 You and your Branwen corrupt this country.

77

Servant 1	The King's banned all travel to Wales. You'll never see your family again.
Servant 3	Never see a soft bed again.
Servant 4	You don't belong . . . never one of us . . .
Servant 1	Never. *(They exit as they see Matholwch entering. He sees Branwen)*
Matholwch	You shouldn't be in here. Who do you think—
Branwen	I think I'm your wife . . . Why? You couldn't even tell me.
Matholwch	You put yourself in this position. You've got yourself to blame. I was willing to overlook the insult but your pride . . . your conduct . . . meant that my people could not forget . . .
Branwen	You didn't even have the courage to tell me yourself. I had to hear it from your servants.
Matholwch	You are forgetting, Branwen . . . There are many women who—
Branwen	I am still your wife. You are blind, Matholwch. Your whole country is raddled with rumour . . . The people don't follow you because you are 'Matholwch the

Wise' but because you have the title of King. Don't tell me I don't know what I'm talking about. Remember I live among the kitchen servants now. I listen to what they say behind your back.

Matholwch   Your tongue shall be silenced.

Branwen   We have spent over a year as man and wife . . . I have borne your son.

Matholwch   And he shall be King.

Branwen   He will be known as the son of a kitchen maid. He will never rule this country with pride.

Matholwch   My people are growing restless . . . you must suffer in the dark corners and the sculleries where you spend your days and your nights shall be spent entertaining the stable boys.

Branwen   Who rules this country? You? Or is it your people? You are weak, Matholwch.

Storyteller 4   In the face of Branwen's defiance, Matholwch tried to humiliate her further. To stop the tongues of the Court, Branwen should be broken. It was no longer enough that she should be a servant . . .

Storyteller 3	Now, a butcher, *(The butcher arrives)* with the blood from the slaughter-house still on his hands was ordered to hit Branwen each day in front of the court.
Servant 1	Everyday, straight from the slaughter sheds.
Servant 2	With the blood still on his hands.
Servant 3	One blow each day.
Servant 4	Such a pretty face.
Servant 5	Blood for blood.
	The butcher goes up to her and caresses her, smears her face, slaps and punches her.
Butcher	And clear up the mess after you.
Branwen	Merch Llŷr, chwaer Brân, Wnaiff neb gymryd hwn wrtha' i, Fydda' i byth yn anghofio.
Brân	*(from his high point)* Branwen. You are the daughter of Llŷr, You are the sister of Brân, No one, no one will take this from you. I will never forget.

Storyteller 2   With all contact between Ireland and Wales stopped, Branwen's humiliation increased.

Storyteller 3   The weak King could think of no other way to maintain his authority but to force Branwen to acknowledge her faults.

Storyteller 2   If horses were the source of his insult, Branwen should be ridden like a mare.

Woman 1   A sorrowful fate has befallen you, Branwen.

Woman 2   A pleasure-less life,
You bird of hunger,
Who once wore silk.

Woman 1   Look at you.

Woman 2   You rag-tag.

Woman 1   You crow.

Woman 3   From wilderness to wilderness
Hopping and scrambling.

Scene 12—The starling

Branwen

Day after day a starling comes to my hand
both of us small birds at a window
He with a dark rainbow in every feather,
takes seed
and crumbs from me,
touches my hand like rainfall
And I tell my name until
he holds its two syllables
of water in his throat

MUSIC and dance of the bird starts

On a prevailing westerly
I throw him into the wind
crying 'Branwen, Branwen'
to the far horizon.
(From a poem by Gillian Clarke)

Branwen *(sings)*

They've taken my tongue so I talk to the birds,
I will sing my song though it cannot be heard.
The birds tell my story of anguish and pain
For they have the freedom I'll never regain.

The things that they've taken
are locked in my mind,
With the hope that one day I'll be able to find,
Those misty Welsh hills, the home I once knew,
My kinsmen, my brother, I have remained true.

The storytellers focus on Brân.

Storyteller 4   When the bird reached Wales, it was heard calling Branwen's name. The letter Branwen had tied under its wing was found and taken to Brân.

Storyteller 1   He sent messengers to raise an army.

Storyteller   When all were assembled he told them of the sorrows that had come to his sister.

Storyteller 3   Leaving seven lords as stewards of the Island of the Mighty, the army agreed to sail for Ireland.

Storyteller3

Roedd llygaid Bendigeidfran dal,
Wedi deall, yn dân;
I hwylio aeth tan hwyl wen,
Ar unwaith i achub Branwen.

Storyteller 2   So great was the fleet of ships gathered that from a distance the masts seemed as winter trees in a forest.

Storyteller 4   With Brân at their head, the great fleet sailed for Ireland.

Scene 13—The Fleet Reaches Ireland

Swineherd   Believe me when I say it, a great island in the sea!

Peasant 1   What?

Swineherd   An island, I tell you! The size of a castle. Perhaps bigger.

Peasant 2   What are you saying?

Swineherd   Trees.

Peasant 2   What?

Swineherd   Trees. A giant must have been pushing them.

Peasant 1   Have you been struck stupid or something?

Swineherd   It's true, I tell you . . .

Peasant 2   Right!

Swineherd   It's true, damn you. Coming from the east. Come on, I'll show you . . .

Company form ship image with the three brothers Efnisien, Nisien and Brân at their head. Spears and masts rise above the company. Company sing:

84

On the silver waves,
Borne on Celtic breeze,
An army of masts like a forest of trees.

People from afar,
Branwen for to take,
An army of men with revenge in their wake.

The crowned head of a giant,
Two lakes upon a mound,
The swords of Welshmen pointing,
Towards the battle ground,
Towards the battle ground.

Passions raised so high,
War cry on the tide,
An army of men naked swords at their side.
Warlords steely-eyed,
Vengeful brothers three,
An army determined to set Branwen free.

The crowned head of a giant,
Two lakes upon a hill,
The shouts of Welshmen hoping,
Irish blood to spill,
Irish blood to spill,

Company clear stage.

Peasant 1   Sweet Green Man! I bet you can't guess
where I've been. Only to see the King
himself. Let me tell you. Right. After
Ciarán and me seeing this island heading

towards us we immediately went to see King Matholwch. We borrowed horses from the stable master and off we went. When we arrived at the castle we were soaking. I have never seen so much rain. I thought we were going to drown for sure. Oh, anyway . . . where was I? Oh! The castle . . . and we were met by two guards so we were. Keifer and Ciarán got scared and run off, but not me. I wasn't scared. Nothing would frighten me. Why, I remember a time when I was face to face with a . . . oh . . . the castle! Well! Then I was let inside and sweet green man I have never seen the like in all my day. I went up to the throne room. Oh, and I forget to tell you . . . oh, never mind. In I went. I went right up to the throne and knelt down on my left knee right before the king. I nearly forgot which knee it was. Then I remembered my mother saying, 'It's left for love and right for spite.' She was full of things like that was my mother. Do you know what she said once? She said . . . Oh, well, anyway I knelt before the king.'
'What is it?' he said. 'Well, I don't know how to tell you this, but there's a great big island coming towards us,' said I. Now I didn't think he believed me so I went on. 'Well, my friend said it was a

rock but rocks don't float, so I assumed it was an island, because of the forest and the lakes and . . .' Then he stopped me. He put his hand on me shoulder and said, 'Say no more . . . you have brought me some excep . . . excep . . . some very important tidings.' He looked very serious. He rewarded me too. Twelve gold coins, he gave, so he did. TWELVE! 'And what about your friends?' said he. 'Well,' I said, 'they did hope that you'd let them look after your pigs.' 'So be it,' he said, all solemn and wise. So I split the twelve gold coins between the three of us which made . . . *(tries to work it out, gives up)* . . . some gold coins each. The boys'll only spend them on pigs, though. Pigs! Only a fool would spend money on pigs. I've got bigger plans: I'm going to buy me . . . A COW. . . . Oh! I nearly forgot. As I was leaving the castle the king called for that Welsh whore. 'BRANWEN,' said he . . .

Scene 14—The Trap

Branwen, Matholwch and Niámh enter.

Matholwch   You have told Brân?

Branwen   The birds of the air know, why should not my brother?

Matholwch   How?

Branwen   The brother will avenge his sister.

Matholwch   Who will avenge Matholwch? Must there be war?

Branwen   Did you really think you could treat a daughter of Llŷr as you have treated me and not spill your country's blood?

Matholwch   *(silence)*

Branwen   May I leave?

Matholwch   Go. *(Then, seeing Niámh, sharply,)* But not to greet your brother: *(draws a dagger)* better you should absent yourself while we prepare to 'welcome' our Welsh guests.

Branwen   *(seeing the dagger)* No. A battle will destroy both our lands . . . Gwern . . . Brân . . . all my brothers, my son . . . Why should the Islands be filled with widows and orphans to assuage my wrongs? I suffer but why should the suffering spread? I will keep silent . . .

Matholwch   It is too late . . . Brân will never forgive us.

Branwen   You forgave the insult of the horses. *(Both pause to reflect on the half-truth of this statement.)*

Matholwch   No. He will be like a giant wasting and ravaging my lands . . . Take her away . . . Keep her close . . . don't let her be seen. *(She is escorted off by a Guard.)*

Storyteller 3   For Matholwch's people still kept the old hatred bubbling.

Storyteller 1   And he knew he had the cauldron.

Storyteller 3   Brân could not defeat him while he could resurrect his warriors in the cauldron of rebirth.

Storyteller 2   A trap had been devised.

Storyteller 3   A peg was fixed to each of the hundred pillars of the hall—and from each peg hung a bag, and in each bag was hidden an armed man.

Storyteller 1   It was the custom at that time that no weapons should be brought into a feast hall. Matholwch planned that once the unarmed, unsuspecting Welsh were seated in the hall, the trap could be sprung.

Storyteller 2   For a second time the kings met.

MUSIC as before. The Irish enter and ceremoniously plunge their swords into the ground at front

Irish 1   You'll stay close to me tonight won't you?

Irish 2   If we live that long.

Irish 3   Surely Matholwch's plans won't fail.

Irish 4   No, the Welsh will be dead by tonight.

Irish 5   Don't one of you even glance at one of those bags.

Irish 6   I wish I was in one of those sacks, waiting, to jump out . . . That's the real warrior's place.

Irish 4   You leave the fighting to those who know how, boy.

Matholwch   Remember, give those soldiers brave enough to be placed in the sacks extra wine and a high place at the victory feast, when it's all over.

Irish 5   I will see to it, my Lord.

Irish 4   I think they're coming.

Matholwch   To your places. Not a word and may those warriors who die in battle gain a reward in Annwn.

(Welsh led by the three brothers enter)

Brân   Greetings, Matholwch the Wise. High King of all Ireland, we come in peace as your guests.

Efnisien   I trust our sister is well

Nisien   We wish to see our nephew, Gwern.

Matholwch   Welcome, Brân the Mighty. Will you feast with us as our guests?

Irish 4   In accordance with our ancient customs all weapons of war will be left at the threshold. You will find ours already there.

Brân   Let us speak together, Matholwch, before the banquet. Let us walk together in fresh air, along the river bank, before we enter the feast hall.

Matholwch   As you would have it, Brân.

They all depart away from the hall except Nisien and Efnisien.

Nisien   You're too suspicious, brother.

Efnisien   Something is wrong, these Irish smile with their lips but not their hearts.

Nisien   Always your doubts.

Efnisien   Too suspicious? Then where is Branwen? Where is our nephew? The boy who will unite our countries.

Nisien   Our sister might be . . .

Efnisien   No, Nisien. Look around you at the faces of our Irish friends, at their watchful faces and their clenched fists. Why did Matholwch look so disappointed when Brân postponed the feast? Nisien, this is my chance, to show the world that Brân was *wrong*. If only he hadn't given the cauldron away . . . Nisien, our time has come.

Storyteller 4   Efnisien entered the hall and went to the sacks.

Storyteller 2   When he asked, the Irish said they were filled with flour.

Storyteller 1	When he felt the head of the warrior within the bag, he crushed it, squeezed it, until his fingers pierced the skull.
Storyteller 3	And he did this to each and every one of the bags until all were dead.
Irish A	He stood there smiling as each sack dripped.
Irish B	Blood on the floor.
Irish C	Blood on his hands.
Irish D	He was smiling.
Irish B	Why didn't they stop him?
Irish E	How could they admit that they had violated the sanctuary of the Feast Hall?
Irish A	Swords and killings in the feast hall . . . who would have thought it?
Irish C	We live in dark times.
Irish B	And they'll get darker.
Irish D	Matholwch will never be trusted again.
Irish B	Wherever we travel the Irish will be watched and followed. We'll be forced to sleep in the ditches, not welcomed as neighbours.

Irish C   Would you trust a man who tries to murder his guests?

Efnisien.   With these two hands I did it. I alone killed them all. Efnisien. Efnisien the warrior. Though he may be a king, Brân is a fool. I saw straight through their plot. One hundred leather bags hanging on the walls. Irish warriors hidden inside. Easy pickings for me. They would have fooled Brân, but not Efnisien. Efnisien the Warrior.

Niámh enters.

With these two hands, I tell you. One by one my hands reached inside the bag, and each time with one strain of my fingers I squeezed my victim's skull, until my fingers were laced with Irish blood. My thirst for blood ran hot.

Niámh   Her fault . . . Branwen . . . the root of all our troubles . . . He looked into her eyes and was ensnared . . . Branwen hangs like an unhappy charm around the neck of Ireland. . . . Shame . . . I could see it inching closer, closer as each sack, each head was squeezed. How could you have known? . . . Did she tell you? . . . Those helpless men of Ireland . . . to die

94

trapped, without the chance to win honour in the fight . . . without any glory . . . You gave them no chance.

Efnisien   Where is my sister?

Niámh   She must have told you.

Efnisien   You must have good harvests in Ireland. Your granaries must be full if you have to hang sacks in the hall.

Niámh   The cauldron is already hot. You forget our warriors can now be reborn.

Efnisien   *(silent)*

Niámh   No more deceits, no more tricks. There will be one last battle, then Ireland can forget this 'Welsh Interlude'.

Efnisien   Brân and Matholwch may still seek peace.

Niámh   Matholwch will listen to his people now.

Efnisien   No, Matholwch still dreams he is a man of peace. 'Matholwch the Peacemaker': that will be his epitaph.

Scene 15—The Last Chance Of Peace

Storyteller 2   So for the third and final time the two high kings met.

MUSIC AS BEFORE (the two kings and their forces confront each other)

Welsh or Irish He still wants to talk.

Welsh or Irish After all that's happened.

Niámh   An apology will never be enough . . . Words can't wipe out the insult.

Brân   Yn enw Ynys y Cedyrn . . .

Matholwch   It was the will of my people.

Brân   Your foolishness could result in the destruction of your kingdom.

Matholwch   Think . . . What could you gain from destroying us? *(Brân doesn't answer)* Maybe we could come to an agreement. Your sister's son . . . my son . . . Gwern could still rule . . . as joint king after us. There is no need for us to fight. He must inherit both our kingdoms. Branwen . . .

Brân turns to draw his sword but Branwen entering with Gwern runs to stop the attack.

Branwen   I suffer, but why must the suffering spread?

Storyteller 1   A king should lead his people not be led by them,

Storyteller 3   And the news was proclaimed:

Storyteller 2   There would be no battle.

Branwen runs to her brother, he takes her hand; she winces as he touches the blisters. He looks at the red hands and stares at Matholwch but still he tries for peace. Gwern enters. Company sing. By the end of the song there is a tableau of the investiture of Gwern, crowned with a circlet by Matholwch and Brân.

Company *(sing)*

A king should be a bridge,
A fo ben bid bont,
On his back a nation thrives,
His strength will lead us on.

A king should be a hawk,
Gwylio'r wlad i gyd,
Protecting creatures far below,
His court a nest of warmth.

A king should be a rock,
Dylai brenin fod yn graig,
A stone that knows a history,
A pillar carved of pride.

A king should be a flame,
Dylai brenin fod yn fflam,
A beacon burning strength and hope,
A torch that lights his land.

A king should be a bridge,
A fo ben bid bont,
On his back a nation thrives,
His strength will lead us on.

Efnisien enters and is stopped by Branwen.

Efnisien   Am I allowed to greet my nephew? . . .
Tywysog Cymru . . . the young prince of
(He deliberately mistranslates) 'Ireland'.
Dere 'ma.
(Getting no reply he gestures, to call his nephew over. Gwern, seeking Matholwch's approval first, goes to him.) Beth sy'n bod arnat ti? . . . S'dim tafod 'da ti? He cannot speak his mother's tongue! *(He suddenly grabs Gwern.)* Before the gods I swear, the deed I do now is one no one but me has thought of . . . Its dread enormity is my

98

own. *(He runs carrying Gwern to the back, Brân stopping Branwen. Shouts from everyone as they run back, covering and surrounding Efnisien.)*

Storyteller 4   Efnisien carried the boy to the fire.

Storyteller 1   Brân's strong arm held Branwen back.

Storyteller 3   And before any could lay hand on him he had plunged the boy into the flames.

Storyteller 1   Now there could be no chance of peace.

From the group Branwen emerges:

Branwen   Brân . . . Brân. Ever-loving, my ever-loving brother who . . . Gwern . . . Brân. His hand so firm, so strong you couldn't . . . I couldn't . . . I'll wake up . . . This carnage, this tragedy . . . Gwern . . . my son, my hope . . . taken from me, by . . . Gone. Efnisien, running and screaming across the hall. He was screaming. And I could have stopped him . . . I could have . . . Brân . . . Brân, Efnisien, fire, death. Gwern. Why? *(Brân emerges from the group at the back).* Why, Brân?

Brân   My nephew's life stolen from us . . . the loss of one so young . . . Question and ask why? . . . Why did Gwern have to die? . . . Why should there not be peace?. Yesterday we asked questions, but today, today is the time to fight. There is no other choice. The coming battle will settle all. Efnisien, we will test your way: by tomorrow we will know whether a battle can ever bring us peace.

Scene 16—The Battle

Company regroup around kings and sing:

Company

    Silence, kings, silence,
    Remember a thousand petty grievances.
    Silence, kings, silence,
    A hundred broken promises,
    A single burning lie.

    Whisper, kings, whisper,
    The names of the damned,
    The souls of tortured men.
    Whisper, kings, whisper,
    The vows of vengeful warriors,
    Unleash the words of hate.

    Speak, kings, speak,
    The orders of soldiers,
    Speak, kings, speak,

Let battle lines be drawn,
Scream, kings, scream,
The songs of the slaughter,
Bent on blood and fire.

Silence, kings, silence,
Remember a thousand petty grievances
Silence, kings, silence
A hundred broken promises, a single burning lie.

The future is built on the bones of the past,
The future is built on the bones of the past.

> *The swords are pulled from the ground and preparations are made for battle.*
> *Screams and noises, images of the battle.*
> *Survivors are male or female warriors and others caught up in battle and its aftermath.*

Nisien Men, women, children—they're all the same to me now . . . we charged like beasts . . . my feet slipped in the mud . . . sweat stung my eyes.

Survivor1 Weary and outnumbered . . . the moist earth beneath our feet making a quagmire in the drizzle . . .

Efnisien The swords dug deep but the cauldron, . . . the cauldron . . .

Storyteller 2   Immediately the battle began the Irish lit a fire under the cauldron. Dead bodies were cast into it until it was full. The dead arose from the cauldron as fighting men, mute and savage. No one could defeat the Irish while the cauldron boiled.

Survivor 2   As soon as a man was cut down . . . they threw him in and he rose up . . . reborn.

Nisien   You fought well.

Survivor 1   What joy is there in this destruction?

Efnisien   If the cauldron hadn't been given we would have overwhelmed them. We would have won with few lost . . . but look at us . . . There can be no joy with so few of us left. We are as dead as the corpses that climb back out of the cauldron.

Nisien   We are living . . . our sister is avenged . . . the sea will be a safe passage.

Survivor 1   But what of the dead? They gave their lives for your family's honour.

Nisien   Not my family's, but our country's honour.

Survivor 1   But our people are not alive to see our country's honour maintained.

Survivors start to move off.

Efnisien   But what of the cauldron? They so nearly won because of Brân's gift. Their dying were living again and our living dying.

Survivor 4   Blood, there's so much blood.

Survivor 5   He was cut at the throat . . . blood dripped down his neck. Then, when he came silently from the cauldron with those dead eyes . . .

Survivor 6   How many times did they die? Each time a different agony . . . Each time, dragged from the peace of the underworld.

Survivor 7   I'm haunted by the endless ghosts of warriors unable to die.

Survivor 8   My brother, they've killed him again . . . his blood . . .

Efnisien   Brân's foolishness has cost our country dear. I, Efnisien, will defend my country's pride. Carry me as if I am dead, lay me amongst the corpses. I will feign death . . . and will be flung into that cursed cauldron. I will finish it.

Nisien   Gwnaf, fy mrawd.

Efnisien   Remember.

*They put their swords down, and brother
embraces brother. Nisien picks up
Efnisien and carries him upstage. Others
run to group around him and his 'body' is
flung into the air. No longer feigning
death, he suddenly stretches and screams
as he falls into the cauldron that is
surrounded and concealed by the crowd.
Niámh emerges from the group to address
Branwen who has remained down stage
front since she asked Brân 'why?'*

Scene 17—The Death Of Brân And Branwen.

Niámh   Efnisien, your brother . . . had the
                   strength of ten men. The noise was
                   unbearable. Inside the cauldron he
                   stretched, pushed against the sides,
                   broke it into pieces . . . along with his
                   heart. I looked into your brother's eyes
                   as he died. Now it will finish.

Survivor 9   I am plagued, tormented by the screams
                   of agony forever.

Survivor 10   A child watching his father draw its last
                   breath. They used poisoned spears. Brân
                   himself was cut.

Survivor 11	Mouths full of blood. Red crows feeding on the dead.
Survivor 12	Swords and spears dragged through the flesh of loyal soldiers
Survivor 11	Brân . . . fifty died by his left hand, fifty by his right. He didn't think it too many.
Survivor 12	Poisoned in the foot by a spear . . . He never knew that Efnisien had shattered the cauldron and we . . .
	Brân enters, supported by warriors.
Brân	Take me back, my place is amongst my warriors.
	He falls, abandoning sword and shield.
Branwen	My brother! *(Turns to him and runs to his broken body, removes his helmet, cradles him.)*
Brân	The spear was poisoned.
Branwen	We had such dreams . . . now broken . . . they lie amongst the pieces of the cauldron.
Brân	I should never have—
Branwen	Sshhh. You did what you had to do. There is no need for blame . . . Nothing can prosper without love.

Brân   Branwen Brydferth. When I die, take my head back to Wales. In Harlech you will feast for seven years. and the birds of Rhiannon shall sing to you. I did not forget . . . *(Dies.)*

Branwen   I shall not forget. Our land will remember.

Storyteller 3   Only the cry of broken women, crying as the cold white moon cuts through the black of the night. Only five pregnant women left from all Matholwch's court.

                    MUSIC. Warriors carry off the body of Brân and take his shield and sword as well. Finally Gwenllian takes the helmet of Brân from Branwen who has been cradling it since the body was taken from her.

Storyteller 1   Cold ash in the hearth. Matholwch's hall was empty that night, the wind whistling through empty corridors . . . cold ash on the tear-stained cheeks of the children.

Storyteller 2   And it came to pass as Brân had commanded

Storyteller 3   They buried the head of Brân the Raven, below the Tower in London, where the ravens still walk to this day.

Storyteller 4　　Ond o! colli 'i brawd ei hun,
　　　　　　　　　Yntau a'i gŵr, a'i phlentyn,
　　　　　　　　　Un gwyn a theg, a wnaeth hon,
　　　　　　　　　A'i harddwch yn Iwerddon.

Dancers begin a dance of sorrow. The following speech is over music and starts as the dance draws to a close.

Branwen　　All gone. My brothers . . . my child . . . my husband. Just seven men left alive. Seven men from Wales . . . proud Welshmen who came across the sea like a forest. How quickly they were chopped down. What I did, I did for my country. I am returning to Wales but what is left for me there? What is left but seven broken men and the head of my brother. What have I suffered? Who can I blame? There is no one. Matholwch should not have taken me as wife, Brân should not have given me. Efnisien? Efnisien, my foolish, foolish brother, you were too proud when you should have understood, too hateful when you should have cared. But I cannot hate you. You are . . . were . . . my brother. Gwern, my sweet son. Born into a land where they could not accept you. You were born to be a bridge between two countries, but nothing can prosper where there is no love. I am Branwen the beautiful, Branwen Brydferth .

Music continues.

Storyteller 2   They sailed at night. They were victorious, but knew they had lost.

Storyteller 4   Knew it but did not speak it.

Storyteller 1   A long journey with brothers, fathers, husbands all gone . . .

MUSIC —echoes of the starling motif

Branwen   I can hear singing. Singing. The song of my starling . . . Branwen! Branwen! I wish I had never sent that bird to Brân. Two islands laid waste because of me.

The dead: Brân, Matholwch, Nisien, Efnisien, appear above as she continues.

Branwen   Branwen. Branwen. What's the use? I have no purpose. I shall never sing again in my brother's court . . . see the fine ships passing by my window . . . those bright, bright fields . . . never watch the red sun sink slowly into the sea . . . No more, Branwen, no more.

Company   *Take up final song. Towards its end Gwenllian comes towards Branwen and, from behind, slowly raises the hood of her cloak. Branwen closes her eyes and sinks back, supported by Gwenllian. She dies as the song ends.*

Lace of a winter ash-tree
in a broken mirror
where the river strums its stones,
combing and combing
its long green hair.

There is weeping here
in the cold stream,
in the crumpled face of water,
in the sob of wind,
in a cry of water-birds.

There's a whirr of air
and a tambourine of birds
rings in a cold sky,
and the ash is leafed again,
the starling tree.

Her memory erased
from the stones
by the wind and and the rain,
her name
on the tongue of a bird.

*(words to the song from a poem
by Gillian Clarke)*

The Music

For the original production of *On the Tongue of a Bird* the band consisted of keyboards, two violins (one doubling oboe), a flute, and a percussionist. In many ways the instrumentation is unimportant; while I have indicated instruments at certain points, the score is by no means cast in tablets of stone. Indeed, all of the music is open to interpretation; but I think a realistic basic requirement would be keyboards, percussion, and a melody insrument. Please feel free to alter, add or take away music to suit your production's needs; you may want to add more dances, for example, or add songs of your own. I hope you have as much fun with the music as we did in the creation of the original production.

John Quirk

REPEAT
TO FADE

113

"BRÂN — HIGH KING OF ALL THE ISLANDS OF THE MIGHTY......" [UNDERSCORE]
(STEADY, BUT WITH UNDERLYING POWER.)

"BLACK SHIPS SLID SILENTLY UP THE RIVER"

"PROUD HORSES"

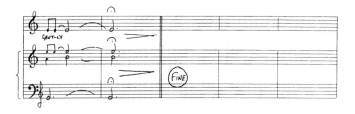

GENT-LY

FINE

"RITUAL CAULDRON MUSIC"

STEADY 3 — SADLY   "ABRASIVE WINDS"

ABRASIVE WINDS p.2

1) A – BRASIVE WINDS 'TEAR AT MY EYES,
2) MY BROTHER LOOKS OUT FROM THE SHORE,

120

PULL AT MY DRESS, THEIR GRIP SO TIGHT. DRAG ME A - WAY, A - WAY FROM HOME.
HIS HIDDEN TEARS BE - HIND HIS SMILE. I LOOK A - HEAD, THE FU - TURE CALLS.

BUT I'M TOO PROUD TO CRY BUT I'M TOO PROUD TO CRY

CODA
WAVES CRASH A - GAINST THE POLISHED DECK SEA WA - TER SCORES MY CHEEK

SPRAY ON MY FACE LIKE SALTY TEARS BUT I'M TOO PROUD TO CRY BUT I'M TOO PROUD TO

CRY

"IRISH DANCE"

123

"DANCE OF WELCOME"

124

"BRANWEN GAVE BIRTH TO A CHILD."

"EYES STARE THROUGH HER"

126

BRANWEN'S SONG – "THE SUN IS RISING"

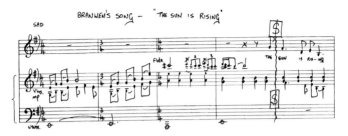

2ND VERSE WORDS [ON D.$.]

"THE SERVANTS STARING, DARING ME TO CRY,
IN MY MIND THEY CANNOT SEE ME,
THERE IS NO LOVE, NO PRAISE, NO HOPE.
WATCHING THE BLEAK HORIZON, WAITING, HOPING."

⊕ CODA

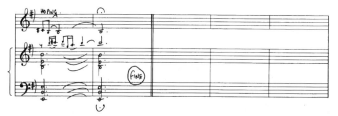

129

"ON THE SILVER WAVES"

GROUND,   TWARD THE BATTLE — GROUND.

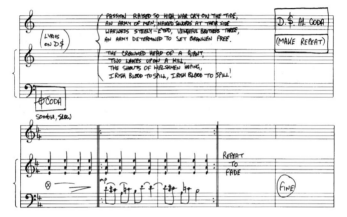

(LYRICS ON D$)

PASSION RAISED SO HIGH, WAR CRY ON THE TIDE,
AN ARMY OF MEN, NAKED SWORDS AT THEIR SIDE
WARLORDS STEELY-EYED, VENGEFUL BROTHERS THREE,
AN ARMY DETERMINED TO SET BRANWEN FREE.

THE CROWNED HEAD OF A GIANT,
TWO WAVES UPON A HILL,
THE SHOUTS OF WELSHMEN HOPING,
IRISH BLOOD TO SPILL, IRISH BLOOD TO SPILL!

D. S. AL CODA

(MAKE REPEAT)

⊕ CODA

SOMBER, SLOW

REPEAT
TO
FADE

(FINE)

132

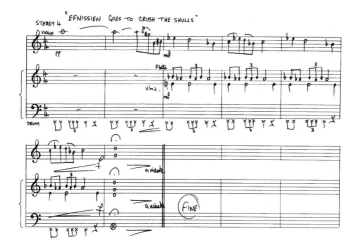

"EFNISSIEN GOES TO CRUSH THE SKULLS"

133

"A KING SHOULD BE A BRIDGE"

STRENGTH AND HOPE, A TORCH THAT LIGHTS HIS LAND A KING SHOULD BE A BRIDGE

A FOR DOWN AND BOUT ON HIS BACK A NA—TION TURNES HIS STRENGTH WILL LEAD US

ON!

FINE

135

"SILENCE, KINGS, SILENCE!"

STEADY - WITH NOBILITY

SIL-ENCE KINGS, SI-LENCE! RE - MEMBER A THOUSAND PETTY GRIEVAN-CES! SIL-ENCE KINGS

SILENCE! A HUN-DRED BRO-KEN PROMISES, A SING-LE BURN-ING LIE!

WHIS-PER KINGS, WHIS-PER THE NAMES OF THE DAMNED, OF TOR-TURED MEN WHIS-PER KINGS
THE SONS

WHIS-PER! THE VOWS OF VENGE-FUL WARRIORS, UN - LEASH THE WORDS OF HATE.

SPEAK KINGS SPEAK! THE OR-DERS OF SOL-DIERS, SPEAK KINGS, SPEAK! LET BATTLE LINES BE DRAWN! SCREAM KINGS, SCREAM THE

136

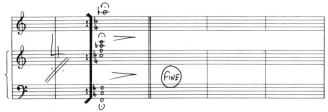

"BRAN'S DEATH"

by ROSHANAK NASEHI

139

Top: Lady Niámh, played by Joanna Williams.
Centre: Efnisien, played by Matthew Thomas.
Bottom: A storyteller played by Chris Bradshaw and dancers Mandy Gay and Chloë Davies watch with Brân as Branwen suffers in Ireland.

A Note on the Company

The West Glamorgan Youth Theatre was founded in 1975 under its first director Godfrey Evans and was closely followed by the formation of the West Glamorgan Youth Dance Company. These Companies have gained a reputation for excellence as premier Youth Companies in Wales. Past members of the Companies have gone on to win Olivier and BAFTA Awards, to star in West End Musicals or to work with the larger national theatre companies as well as on television. However, the Companies have never been seen merely as a training ground for the theatre. Many students go on to different, equally successful careers. All look back on their time with the Companies as being an exciting and vital part of their education.

The very existence of these Companies allows young people of ability and talent to have the opportunity to work together under the guidance of specialist tutors in a residential setting. For both Companies the main focus is the rehearsal and creation of a performance but underpinning this work are studio classes. The residential experience with its enhanced opportunities for young people to develop both socially and intellectually has always been central to the Companies' work. The performances that grow from this process have achieved critical acclaim both nationally and internationally during European tours.

The Writing of the Play

The play was created during a five-day residential course at Danycoed Educational Centre, during the Easter holidays. During the summer term the group continued to submit ideas and draft scenes when they were not revising for GCSE or A-level examinations. At the end of the summer term the Company was augmented with dancers, technicians and musicians for a fifteen-day residential course that included the final redrafting of the text, rehearsals and the first performances. The Company consisted of forty-two young people with ages ranging between 14 and 19.

In addition to the cast-list that appears on p. 19 the following personnel were involved:

142

ON THE TONGUE OF A BIRD

Written and Devised by the Company

Conceived and Directed by **Derek Cobley**
with **Kevin Matherick** and **Ruth Williams**
Original Music Composed and Directed by **John Quirk**
and the Company
Choreography by **Douglas Comley** and **Julie Hobday**
Musicians
Katie Fabricius, Nia Lewis, Roshanak Nasehi, Sian Parker, Damien Rees
Technicians
Stage Manager: **Donna Reeves**
Assistant Stage Manager: **Robbie Davies**
Managers: **Chloë Morgan, Simon Davies, Leanna Davies**
Wardrobe Mistress: **Helen Forde**
Wardrobe Assistants: **Lucy Chaves, Sarah Mainwaring**

Tutorial and Residential Staff

Acting and Devising	**Derek Cobley**
	Kevin Matherick
	Ruth Williams
Dance	**Douglas Comley**
	Julie Hobday
Wardrobe	**Mary Pugh**
Technical	**Adrian Hocking**
	Jeff Lewis
Music	**John Quirk**
Administration	**Mary Devoy**
Student Tutors	**Nick Evans**
	Tonya Smith
	Richard Jones
Student Company Manager	**Chris Lindsay**

Running time with music and dance, no interval: one hour, forty minutes approx.

Top: Lady Niámh challenges Matholwch.

Centre: butcher, servants and Gwenllian (Jennifer Walker) at the Irish court.
Bottom: women listen to news of the cutting of the horsest.